THE ULTIMATE
CHICK FLI
Songbook

—— JUST WHAT A GIRL WANTS! ——

Wise Publications
part of The Music Sales Group
London/New York/Paris/Sydney/Copenhagen/Berlin/Madrid/Tokyo

Published by
Wise Publications
8/9 Frith Street, London W1D 3JB, UK.

Exclusive Distributors:

Music Sales Limited
Distribution Centre, Newmarket Road, Bury St Edmunds,
Suffolk IP33 3YB, UK.

Music Sales Pty Limited
120 Rothschild Avenue, Rosebery, NSW 2018, Australia.

Order No. AM984500
ISBN 1-84609-313-9
This book © Copyright 2006 Wise Publications,
a division of Music Sales Limited.

Music arranged by Jack Long
Music processed by Paul Ewers Music Design
Cover photograph courtesy SNAP/Rex Features
Cover design by Josh Labouve
Compiled by Nick Crispin
Printed in the EU

Your Guarantee of Quality

As publishers, we strive to produce every book
to the highest commercial standards.

This book has been carefully designed to minimise
awkward page turns and to make playing from it a real pleasure.

Particular care has been given to specifying acid-free, neutral-sized paper
made from pulps which have not been elemental chlorine bleached.

This pulp is from farmed sustainable forests
and was produced with special regard for the environment.

Throughout, the printing and binding have been planned to ensure a sturdy,
attractive publication which should give years of enjoyment.

If your copy fails to meet our high standards, please inform us
and we will gladly replace it.

www.musicsales.com

Brown Eyed Girl / SLEEPING WITH THE ENEMY 4

Cry To Me / DIRTY DANCING 8

Dreams / BOYS ON THE SIDE / YOU'VE GOT MAIL 12

Feelin' Love / CITY OF ANGELS 22

The Glory Of Love / BEACHES 28

I Say A Little Prayer / MY BEST FRIEND'S WEDDING 32

I Still Haven't Found What I'm Looking For / RUNAWAY BRIDE 17

If You're Not The One / MAID IN MANHATTAN 36

Independent Women Part I / CHARLIE'S ANGELS 42

Jump (For My Love) / LOVE ACTUALLY 48

Just A Ride / MONSTER-IN-LAW 60

Let's Hear It For The Boy / FOOTLOOSE 64

Mona Lisa / MONA LISA SMILE 70

Not Of This Earth / BRIDGET JONES'S DIARY 74

Oh, Pretty Woman / PRETTY WOMAN 80

One Way Or Another / MEAN GIRLS 55

Only Hope / A WALK TO REMEMBER 86

Part Of Me, Part Of You / THELMA & LOUISE 90

Respect / TWO WEEKS' NOTICE / BRIDGET JONES'S DIARY 96

Run To You / THE BODYGUARD 99

Somewhere My Baby Waits For Me / THE WEDDING PLANNER 104

Stop! / BRIDGET JONES: THE EDGE OF REASON 114

Sway / SHALL WE DANCE? 109

Take My Breath Away / TOP GUN 124

A Thousand Miles / LEGALLY BLONDE 118

To Make You Feel My Love / HOPE FLOATS 129

Unchained Melody / GHOST 134

What A Girl Wants / WHAT WOMEN WANT 138

When You Say Nothing At All / NOTTING HILL 144

A Wink And A Smile / SLEEPLESS IN SEATTLE 154

You're The One That I Want / GREASE 150

Brown Eyed Girl

Words & Music by Van Morrison

7

Cry To Me

Words & Music by Bert Russell

Dreams

Words by Dolores O'Riordan
Music by Dolores O'Riordan & Noel Hogan

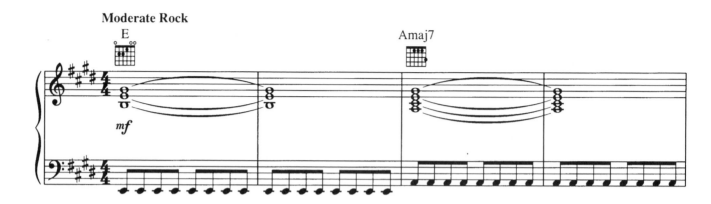

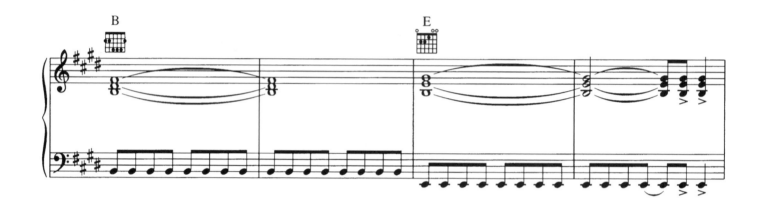

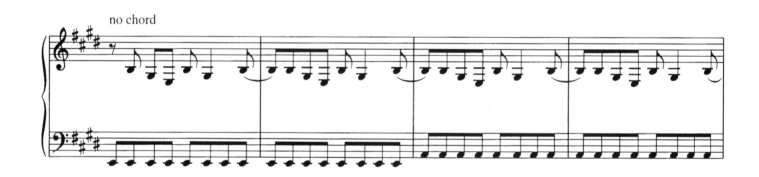

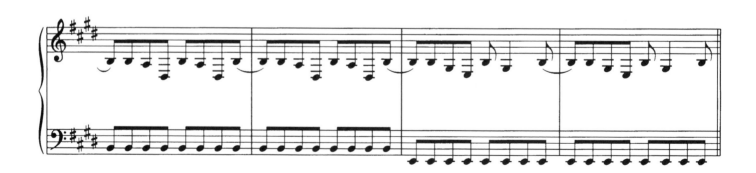

but now I'm feel - ing it e - ven more __ be - a
the per - son fall - ing here __ is me, __ You're
you have my heart __ so don't hurt me. __ you're
so un - der - stand - ing and __ so kind; __

cause it came __ from you. __
dif - f'rent way __ to be. __
what I could - n't find. __
ev - 'ry - thing __ to me. __

Last time To Coda ⊕

Ah, _____ la ____ da

ah, _____ la da ya, _____

14

I Still Haven't Found What I'm Looking For

Words & Music by U2

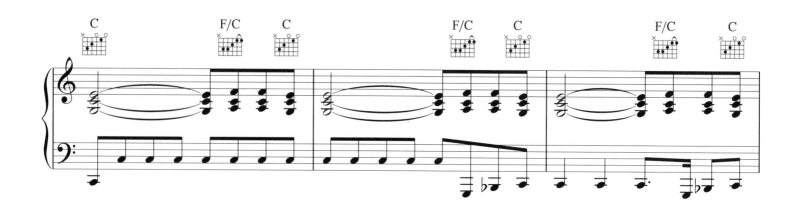

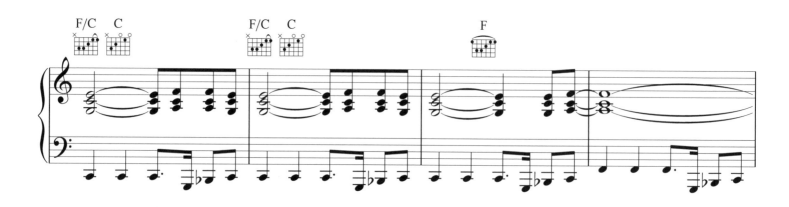

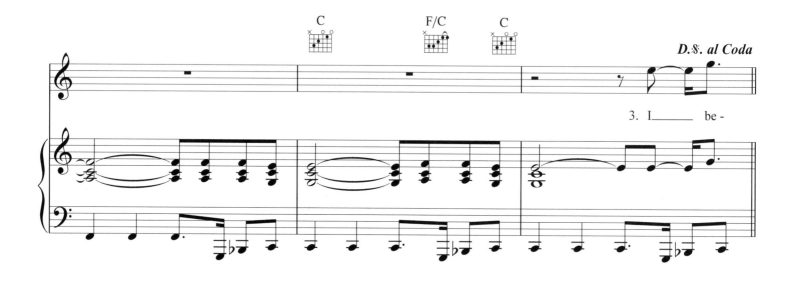

3. I_____ be -

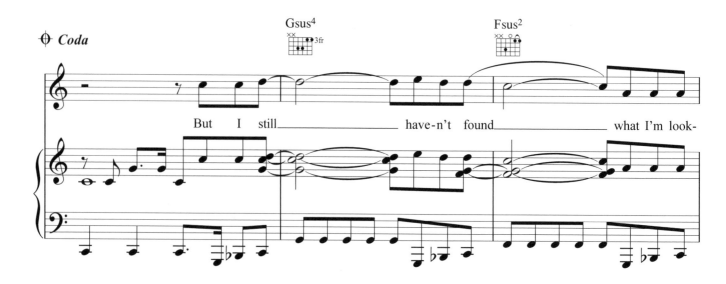

But I still_____ have-n't found_____ what I'm look-

Feelin' Love

Words & Music by Paula Cole

feel like the A-ma-zon's run-ning be-tween my thighs.
op - en the door and___ tie___ me up___ to the bed.

You make me feel

love, love,___ love, love,___ love, love, love,___ love, love,___

love. You make me feel love, love,___ love, love,___ love,

love, love, love, love, love.

2. You make me

Lov - er, I don't know who I am.

Am I Bar - ry White? Am I I -

The Glory Of Love

Words & Music by Billy Hill

that's the glo-ry of love._____

You've got to laugh a lit-tle,_____

cry a lit-tle,_____ un-til the clouds roll by a lit-tle:_____

that's the sto-ry of, that's the glo-ry of love.

I Say A Little Prayer

Words by Hal David
Music by Burt Bacharach

Not too fast, smoothly

I'm— in love with you._____ Ans-wer my prayer._____ Say you love me too._____

Verse 2:
I run for the bus, dear
While riding I think of us, dear.
I say a little prayer for you.
At work I just take time
And all through my coffee break time
I say a little prayer for you.

If You're Not The One

Words & Music By Daniel Bedingfield

40

Independent Women Part I

Words & Music by Beyonce Knowles, Samuel Barnes,
Corey Rooney & Jean Claude Olivier

Tell me what you think a - bout me. I buy my own dia-monds and I buy my own rings. On-ly ring your

(Verse 2 see block lyric)

cell - y when I'm feel-in' lone - ly. When it's all ov - er please get up and leave. Ques-tion:

Tell me how you feel a-bout this. Try to con - trol me boy, you get dis - missed. Pay my own

fun and I pay my own bills, al-ways fif - ty, fif-ty in re - la - tion - ships. The

43

45

Verse 2:

Tell me how you feel about this
Who would I want if I would wanna live
I worked hard and sacrificed to get what I get
Ladies, it ain't easy bein' independent
Question: How'd you like this knowledge that I brought
Braggin' on that cash that he gave you is to front
If you're gonna brag make sure it's your money you flaunt
Depend on no-one else to give you what you want.

The shoes on my feet *etc.*

Jump (For My Love)

Words & Music by Marti Sharron, Gary Skardina & Steven Mitchell

1. Your eyes___ tell___ me how you

want me; I can feel__ it in your heart - beat.

I know_ you like__ what you see.

2. Hold me,__ I'll give_ you all that you need.
(3.) told me__ I'm the on - ly wo - man for you;

Wrap_ your love a - round me. You're so ex - cit - ed I can
no - bo - dy does it like I do. Then make a move be - fore you

I know my heart can make you hap - py.____ (Jump in.)

You know these arms, they fill you up. (Jump.)

If you wan - na taste my kiss - es in the night, then____

jump____ for____ my love.____

N.C.

Repeat to fade

One Way Or Another

Words & Music by Deborah Harry & Nigel Harrison

Just A Ride

Written by by Jem Griffiths & Mike Caren
Contains a sample from 'An Elephant Called Slowly' by Howard Blake

1. Life, it's ev-er so strange___ it's so full of change.___ Think that you've worked___
2. Truth, we don't wan-na hear,___ it's too much to take,___ don't like to feel___
3. Slow-ly, oh, so ve-ry slow-ly ex-cept that there's no get-

62

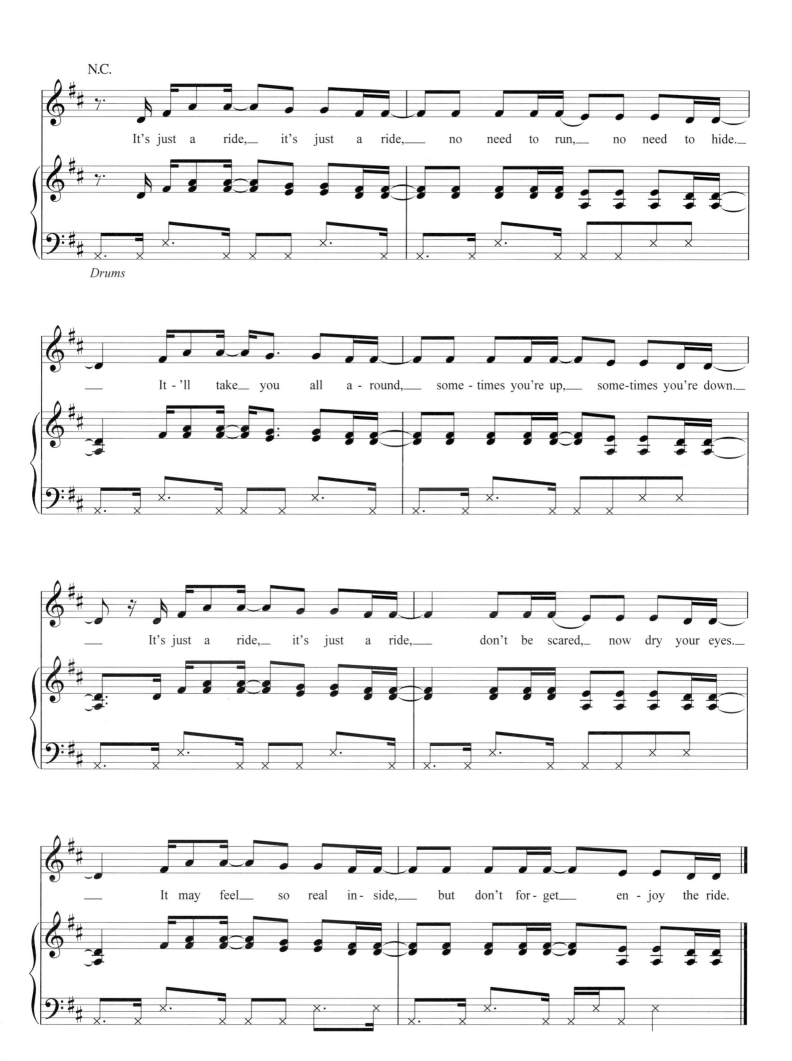

Let's Hear It For The Boy

Words & Music by Dean Pitchford & Tom Snow

'Cause

D.S. al Coda

ev - 'ry time___ he pulls me near I just wan - na cheer,___ "Let's

68

Mona Lisa

Words & Music by Jay Livingston & Ray Evans

Not Of This Earth

Words & Music by Robbie Williams & Guy Chambers

Verse 2:
Not of this earth
She came walking down my lane
I've learnt to laugh again
Like a moth to a flame
Not of this earth
Not surprised we're unashamed
She's gonna have to change her name
Then we'll know that we're the same.

She is not of this earth
And I believe we've seen the worst
If I ever leave this world
You will have a song to sing
So you'll know what you're worth.

Verse 3:
As verse 1.

Oh, Pretty Woman

Words & Music by Roy Orbison & Bill Dees

Pret - ty wo - man stop a while,— pret - ty wo - man
Pret - ty wo - man, yeah yeah yeah,— pret - ty wo - man

talk a while,_____ pret - ty wo - man give your smile— to
look my way,_____ pret - ty wo - man say you'll stay— with

1. me._____ **2.** me._____ 'Cause I

need you, I'll treat you right.

I guess I'll go on home it's late, There'll be to-mor-row night, but wait, what do I see? Is she walk-ing back to me.

Yeah, she's walk - ing back to me.

Oh, _____ pret-ty wo-man.

A

Verse 2:
Pretty woman, won't you pardon me?
Pretty woman, I couldn't help but see,
Pretty woman,
That you look lovely as can be,
Are you lonely just like me?

Verse 3:
Pretty woman, don't walk on by,
Pretty woman, don't make me cry,
Pretty woman,
Don't walk away, hey.

Only Hope

Words & Music by Jonathan Foreman

Part Of Me, Part Of You

Words & Music by Jack Tempchin & Glenn Frey

92

Respect

Words & Music by Otis Redding

Run To You

Words & Music by Jud Friedman & Allan Rich

Somewhere My Baby Waits For Me

Words & Music by Carole King & Gerry Goffin

Sway

Words & Music by Pablo Beltran Ruiz

Stop!

Words & Music by Samantha Brown, Gregg Sutton & Bruce Brody

A Thousand Miles

Words & Music by Vanessa Carlton

1,3. Mak-ing my way down town, walk-ing fast;
(Verse 2 see block lyric)

— fac-es pass,_ and I'm home-bound.

Verse 2:
It's always times like these
When I think of you
And I wonder if you ever think of me.
'Cause everything's so wrong
And I don't belong
Living in your precious memory.
'Cause I need you
And I miss you
And now I wonder:

If I could fall into the sky *etc.*

Take My Breath Away

Words by Tom Whitlock
Music by Giorgio Moroder

125

128

To Make You Feel My Love

Words & Music by Bob Dylan

132

earth for you,___ make you hap-py, make your dreams come true,___

to make you feel my love.___

Unchained Melody

Words by Hy Zaret
Music by Alex North

What A Girl Wants

Words & Music by Shelly Peiken & Guy Roche

When You Say Nothing At All

Words & Music by Don Schlitz & Paul Overstreet

me when-ev-er I fall._____

You_ say it best when you say no-thing at all._____

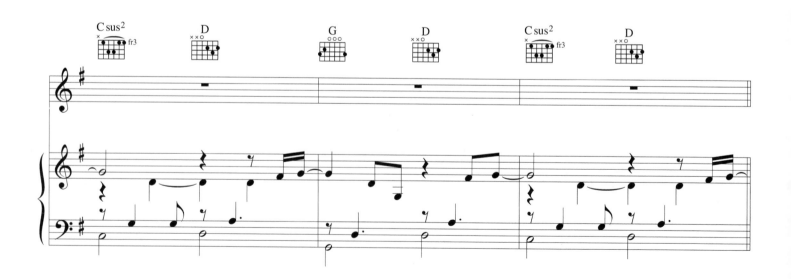

You're The One That I Want

Words & Music by John Farrar

it's e - lec - tri - fy - in'!

(2.) (Feel your way)

C   Em

(Female) You bet - ter shape up, 'cos I need a man,

Am   F

and my heart is set on you.

C

You bet - ter shape up, you bet - ter un -

you, oo, oo, hon-ey. The one that I want,

you, oo, oo are what I need,—

1.

oh yes in - deed.

2. *D.𝄋. to fade*

(Female) 2. If you're

You're the

Verse 2:
(Female) If you're filled with affection you're too shy to convey,
Meditate in my direction, feel your way.

(Male) I better shape up 'cos you need a man,
(Female) I need a man who can keep me satisfied.
(Male) I better shape up if I'm gonna prove,
(Female) You'd better prove that my faith is justified.

(Male) Are you sure?
(Both) Yes, I'm sure down deep inside.

You're the one *etc.*

A Wink And A Smile

Words & Music by Marc Shaiman & Ramsey McLean

miles.

2. Well, you can't have a dream_____ and
5. *Intrumental till* *

cut it to fit,___ but when I saw you___ I knew_____ we'd go to-

-geth - er___ like a wink_ and a smile.___
We_ go to-geth - er___ like a wink_ and a smile.___

Leave your old_____ ja - lo - py___
Now___ my heart___ is mu - sic,___

-geth - er___ with a wink_ and a smile.___

We___ go to-geth - er___ like a wink_ and a

smile.